RAIDERS OF THE SEAS

Written by

JACK BOOTH

Illustrated by

MIKE ROOTH

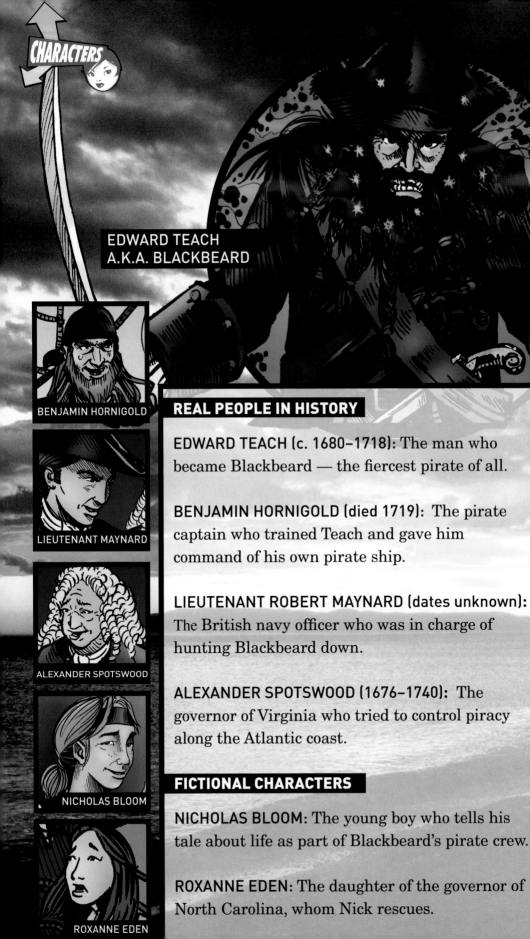

**EDWARD TEACH
A.K.A. BLACKBEARD**

BENJAMIN HORNIGOLD

LIEUTENANT MAYNARD

ALEXANDER SPOTSWOOD

NICHOLAS BLOOM

ROXANNE EDEN

REAL PEOPLE IN HISTORY

EDWARD TEACH (c. 1680–1718): The man who became Blackbeard — the fiercest pirate of all.

BENJAMIN HORNIGOLD (died 1719): The pirate captain who trained Teach and gave him command of his own pirate ship.

LIEUTENANT ROBERT MAYNARD (dates unknown): The British navy officer who was in charge of hunting Blackbeard down.

ALEXANDER SPOTSWOOD (1676–1740): The governor of Virginia who tried to control piracy along the Atlantic coast.

FICTIONAL CHARACTERS

NICHOLAS BLOOM: The young boy who tells his tale about life as part of Blackbeard's pirate crew.

ROXANNE EDEN: The daughter of the governor of North Carolina, whom Nick rescues.

Contents

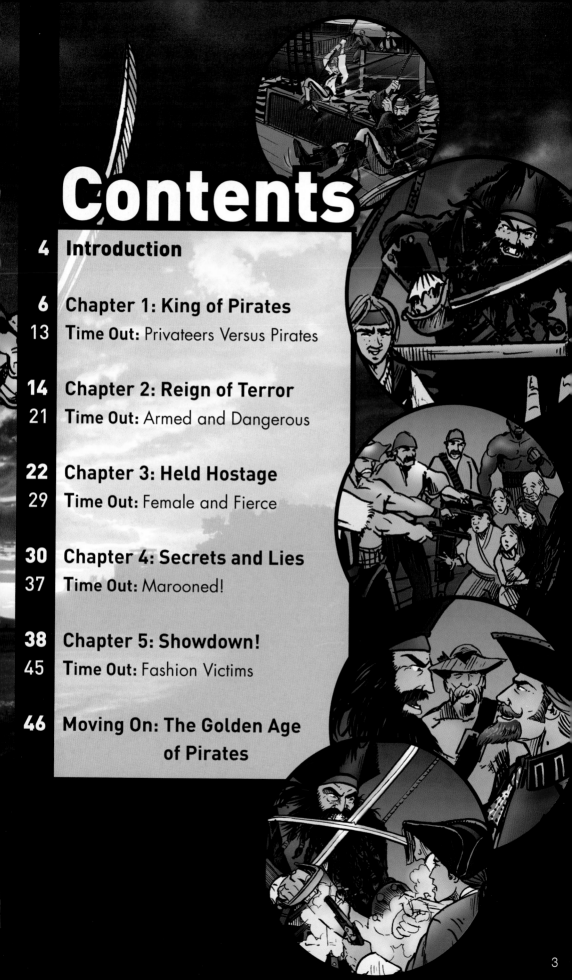

Forget Captain Hook and those Hollywood pirates with their cute little parrots. Blackbeard and his crew were the original gangsters. They were fierce and brutal, and they devoted their lives to the pursuit of pleasure and treasure.

Three hundred years ago, pirates ruled the waters of the Caribbean and the eastern coast of the New World. These vicious crews attacked and robbed the rich trading ships that crossed their paths.

The successful pirate captains captured amazing hoards of treasure and lived like kings. The most terrifying of these was Blackbeard.

TIMELINE

1680 »	1701 »	1713 »	1716 »
Generally considered to be the year the golden age of pirates begins.	Captain Kidd, a famous pirate, is caught and hanged. His treasure is never found.	It was some time after this date that Edward Teach (later Blackbeard) becomes an English privateer — a legal pirate.	Teach joins the crew of Captain Benjamin Hornigold, a well-known pirate.

In this story, young Nicholas Bloom has some tough decisions to make. He starts his sailing career as a privateer — a legal pirate who works for a country and shares the loot with the monarch. Somehow, Nick ends up joining Blackbeard (never a good thing) and as Nick learns, life as Blackbeard's right-hand man isn't always easy.

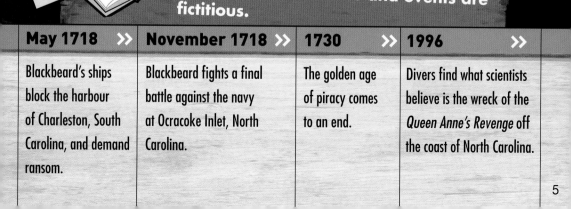

WHAT'S THE STORY?

This story is set in an actual time in history and depicts real people, but some of the characters and events are fictitious.

May 1718 >>	November 1718 >>	1730 >>	1996 >>
Blackbeard's ships block the harbour of Charleston, South Carolina, and demand ransom.	Blackbeard fights a final battle against the navy at Ocracoke Inlet, North Carolina.	The golden age of piracy comes to an end.	Divers find what scientists believe is the wreck of the *Queen Anne's Revenge* off the coast of North Carolina.

PRIVATEERS VERSUS PIRATES

What are privateers? When warring countries wanted to get back at one another, sometimes they chose to hire private ships to help them attack their enemies secretly. This way, they wouldn't have to fight an open war!

So what was the difference between privateers and pirates?

PRIVATEERS
- Were given permission from the government to attack ships
- Only did this in wartime and against ships of an enemy nation
- Got a share of whatever cargo they seized as payment, while the rest went right back to their "boss"

PIRATES
- Were outlaws of all nations, considered criminals
- Attacked anyone at any time
- Stole almost everything they found. Sometimes they would share and sometimes they wouldn't — there were no rules!

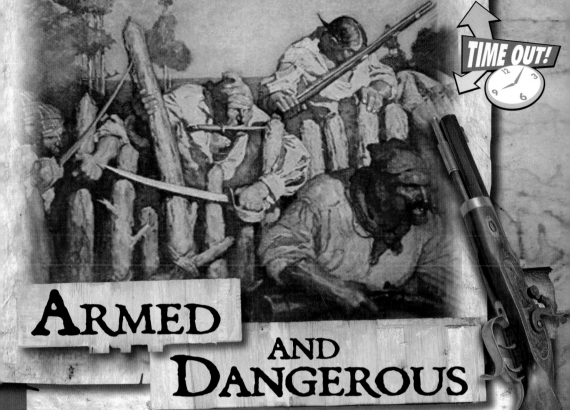

Armed
AND
Dangerous

Blackbeard's fierce attitude earned him a terrifying reputation. Of course, using most of these weapons probably helped a bit, too!

Cutlass: These swords were usually about half a metre long with a slightly curved blade. The short length made them useful for fighting in the close quarters of a ship.

Blunderbuss: A crude shotgun that could hit several people with a single blast (especially on a crowded ship's deck).

Flintlock Pistol: This gun was smaller than the blunderbuss. Pirates would carry several of these because they could fire only one shot at a time.

Cannon: Most cannons needed a crew of three or four men to properly aim, fire, and reload. The cannonballs came in sizes anywhere from "two pounders" to 10 kg "shipwreckers."

Stinkpot: Just as gross as it sounds, these small pots were filled with burning sulphur and rotten fish, and then thrown onto a ship's deck.

FEMALE

AND FIERCE

Women pirates were rare. At the time of this story, women were not allowed on ships — they were considered bad luck. But pirates were rebels who didn't obey the rules. A few women dressed up as men and joined pirate crews.

In November 1720, on the island of Jamaica, three pirates were brought to trial. One pirate, Calico Jack Rackham, was found guilty and hanged. The other two were let off when it was found that they were both expecting babies. Their names were Mary Read and Anne Bonny.

In their pirate lives, Mary Read and Anne Bonny had fought with cutlasses, axes, and pistols. They are the best-known women pirates of all time.

MAROONED!

Pirate crews usually agreed to follow a set of rules while on the ship. However, if a pirate broke the rules by stealing from other crew members or deserting during a battle, he would be left behind or marooned on a desert island.

The marooned sailor was given a bottle of water, a pistol or a musket, and a small amount of shot and gunpowder. He usually didn't survive for long.

The fictional character Robinson Crusoe was based on the true story of Alexander Selkirk. Marooned, Selkirk survived for five years on an island before being rescued. For company on the island, he tamed wild goats and cats. He even taught them to dance.

In this story, Blackbeard stranded the crew of the *Queen Anne's Revenge* on the sandbar so he wouldn't have to share the booty. This was not quite the same as being marooned.

Fashion Victims

The clothes make the man — and pirates were no exception! Just like today's celebrities, pirates knew the importance of a good (or scary!) image. Check out the hottest styles from piracy's Golden Age!

HATS: The more stylish pirates wore a three-cornered hat called a tricorne. Others just wore bandanas around their heads to keep the sweat from dripping into their eyes.

EARRINGS: Some pirates thought that wearing earrings prevented them from getting seasick. Others believed that wearing gold and silver in their ears gave them better vision.

COATS: Pirates usually wore long woollen coats. Near the end of the 1600s, these coats became much shorter in length and were sometimes called "bum-freezers."

GUNS: Since their guns would fire only one shot before they had to be reloaded, pirates often wore silk sashes with several guns attached to them.

FOOTWEAR: Surprisingly, many pirates went barefoot to get better traction on the ship's deck and rigging.

PANTS: In the old days, pants were known as breeches. They were usually loose-fitting and ankle- or calf-length.

THE GOLDEN

AGE OF PIRATES

Though Nicholas Bloom is a fictional character, some of the people he met in the story actually lived during the golden age of pirates. Benjamin Hornigold, Stede Bonnet, and of course, Edward Teach (who became Blackbeard), were actual pirates. Lieutenant Robert Maynard was sent to put an end to Blackbeard, and he did, inflicting numerous sword and bullet wounds!

Paintings and engravings made at the time show Blackbeard with smoking fuses in his hair and beard, and with swords and pistols stuck in his belts. He has been the subject of books, movies, and documentaries on TV.

Blackbeard's ship, the *Queen Anne's Revenge*, was discovered underwater near Beaufort, North Carolina in 1996. It is now a major tourist attraction.

INDEX